THE EMOJI MOVIE: 2018 A CENTUM BOOK 978-1-911460-70-1
Published in Great Britain by Centum Books Ltd
Centum Books, 20 Devon Square, Newton Abbot, Devon, TQ12 2HR, UK.
books@centumbooksltd.co.uk
CENTUM BOOKS Limited Reg. No. 07641486
This edition published 2017. Printed in China.
A CIP catalogue record for this book is available from the British Library.

2018

Write your name here.

This book belongs to

centum

Meet the Emojis

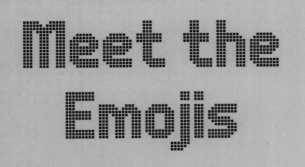

Mel Meh

Is: Gene's Meh dad
Shows: no emotion
Is hiding: a secret malfunction
Looks: a bit Meh

Gene Meh

Is: a Meh
Looks: emotional
Wants: to be normal and just be Meh
Always: doubts himself

Mary Meh

Is: Gene's Meh mum
Acts: like she doesn't care
Wants: to protect Gene
Never: expresses her true self

Hi-5

Is: a hand
Likes: to show some skin
Wants: to be a favourite again
Always: thinks of himself

Smiler

Is: the boss of the cube
Acts: happy at all times
Never: looks how she feels
Always: smiles

Jailbreak

Is: a rebel
Wants: to reach the Cloud
Is hiding: her princess crown
Always: looks out for Number 1

Express yourself

Create your own Emoji in the space below, then fill in the page opposite with everything that is special about you.

Draw your Emoji here.

Give it your favourite colours.

Think up a fun name for your Emoji and write it here.

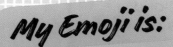

My Emoji is:

happy	sad	funny	cute	a rebel	shy	loud	smart	loved
☐	☐	☐	☐	☐	☐	☐	☐	☐

name:

nickname:

birthday: age:

year born: star sign:

home town/city:

Snapchat/IG handle:

#BeDifferent

How I feel about my...

	friends	family	life	school
♥	☐	☐	☐	☐
👍	☐	☐	☐	☐
👽	☐	☐	☐	☐
😟	☐	☐	☐	☐

best friend:

pets:

biggest achievement:

proudest moment:

most embarrassing moment:

best thing about me:

Textopolis

Can you help Gene find his way through the streets of Textopolis to join the other Emojis?

Smile like you mean it!

FINISH

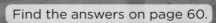

Find the answers on page 60.

Seek and find

Eyes down, blink a few times then see if you can find all the Emojis below in the cube.

#WhatEvs!

**Gene
Meh**

**Loving
Heart**

**Thumbs
Up**

Hammer

Alien

**Angry
Coffee**

Cookie

Dice

How many AV Bots can you spot lurking in the cube?

#YumYum!

Flamenco Girl	**Lipstick**	**Hi-5**	**Jailbreak**	**Slobbering Puppy**	**Donut**	**Glasses**	**Rocket**

Find the answers on page 60.

13

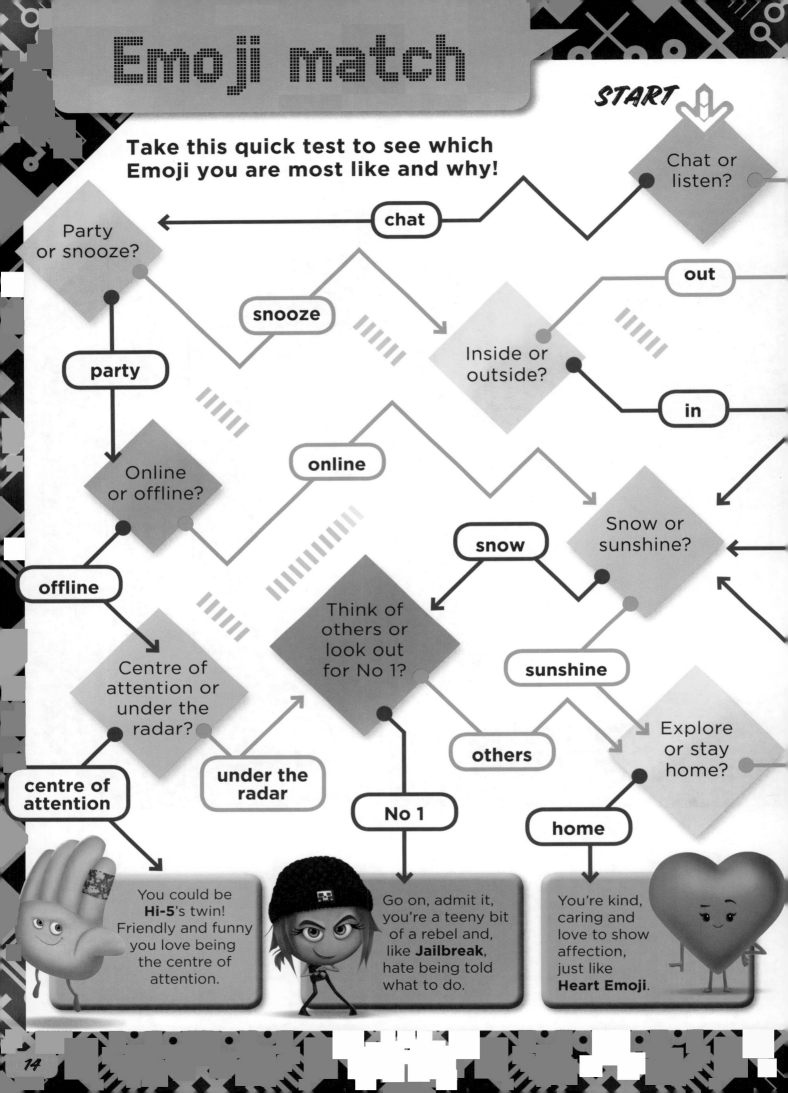

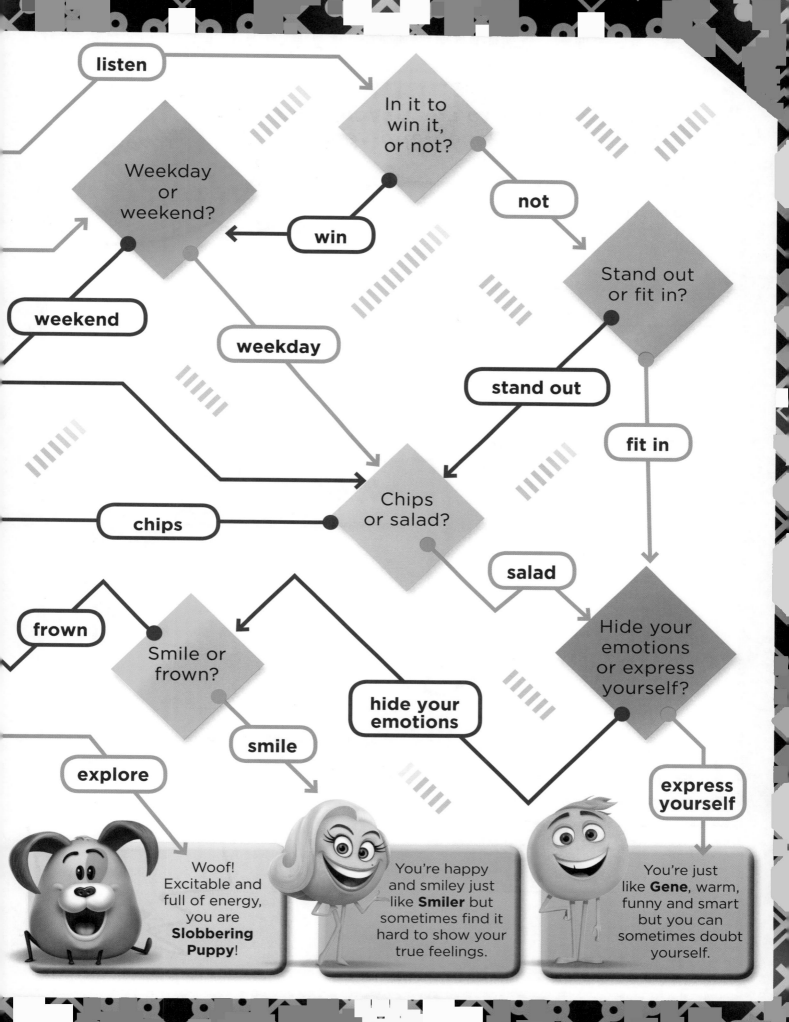

listen

In it to
win it,
or not?

Weekday
or
weekend?

not

win

Stand out
or fit in?

weekend

weekday

stand out

fit in

chips

Chips
or salad?

salad

frown

Smile or
frown?

hide your
emotions

Hide your
emotions
or express
yourself?

smile

explore

express
yourself

Woof!
Excitable and
full of energy,
you are
**Slobbering
Puppy**!

You're happy
and smiley just
like **Smiler** but
sometimes find it
hard to show your
true feelings.

You're just
like **Gene**, warm,
funny and smart
but you can
sometimes doubt
yourself.

Emoji app-venture

Grab your pens to create your own comic strip of Gene's app-venture!

Technology is really amazing!

Gene Meh is different to all of the other Emojis in Textopolis...

_____

_____

_____

_____

_____

_____

_____

#Arghhhhh!

#HolyDeleto ?!

_____

_____

_____

_____

_____

Emoji escape

1
2
3
4
5

Which path should Gene take to escape the cube and reach his pal Hi-5?

Which path leads to the AV Bots?

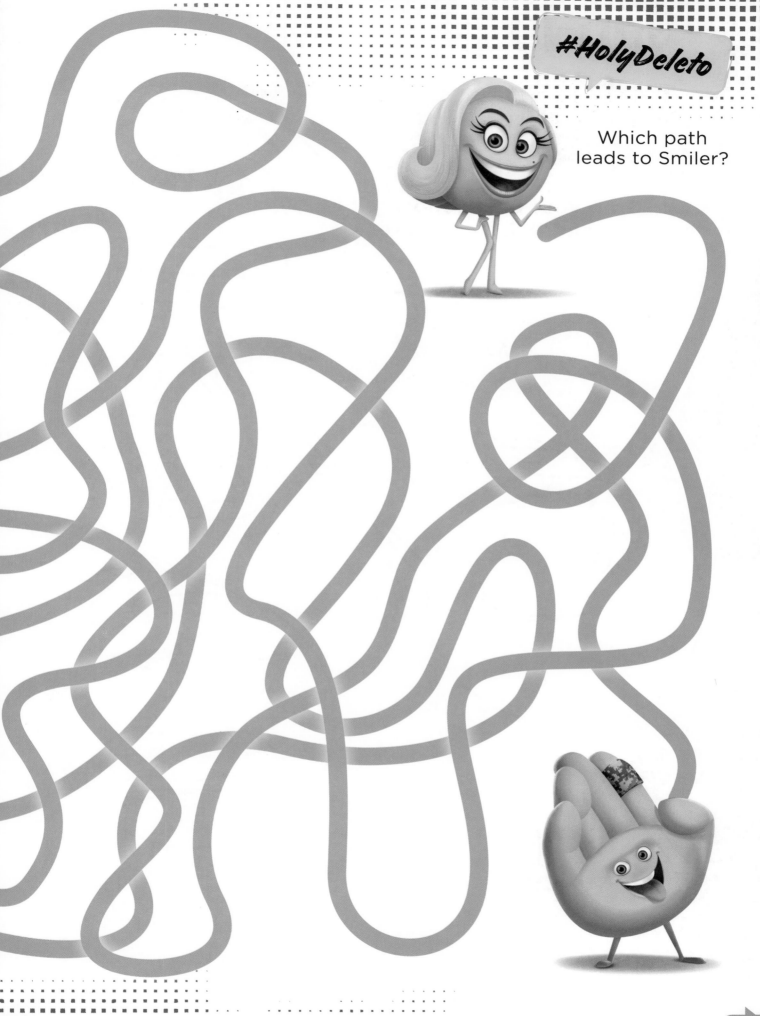

#HolyDeleto

Which path leads to Smiler?

Find the answers on page 60.

Gen-ius colours

Grab your best yellow pen and finish off these pics of Gene.

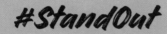

#StandOut

Fit in

Can you fit all the phrases below into the grid opposite?

HOLYDELETO ☐

GIRL BOSS ☐

BE DIFFERENT ☐

BE WEIRD ☐

THE CLOUD ☐

SO EMO ☐

BE YOU ☐

FAVOURITE ☐

EXPRESS YOURSELF ☐

STICK TO EMOJIS ☐

Find the answers on page 60.

Doodle time

Keep doodling Emojis till you fill the page.

Words don't always cut it!

Food fans

Yum! Yum!

Follow these simple steps to make these tasty cookies, then fill in the opposite page with all your fave foods.

What you need:

125g butter
100g light brown soft sugar
125g caster sugar
1 egg, lightly beaten
1 tsp vanilla extract
225g self-raising flour
200g chocolate chips

I need my cookie fix!

What you do:

1 Ask a grown-up to turn on the oven and pre-heat it to 180 degrees/Gas Mark 4.

2 Cream (mix well) the butter and sugars together then add the egg and vanilla.

3 Sift in the flour, then add the chocolate chips.

4 Wrap in clingfilm and leave in the fridge for 30 mins.

5 Take out of the fridge and roll into a long sausage shape, then slice to make neat cookies.

6 Place on a greased baking tray and pop into the oven for 7 to 10 minutes, depending on how chewy you like your cookies.

How I feel about...

	veg	meat	fruit	chocolate
(heart)	☐	☐	☐	☐
(thumbs up)	☐	☐	☐	☐
(lips)	☐	☐	☐	☐
(worried)	☐	☐	☐	☐

#PizzaNight

fave food: ....

for breakfast I love to eat: ....

school dinners ☐ or packed lunch ☐

snack before bed?

yes ☐ no ☐

best cook in the family:

worst cook in the family:

Odd Emoji out

Can you spot the odd Emoji out in each row below?

	A	B	C	D	E	F	
1							
2							
3							
4							
5							
6							
7							
8							

Now circle the two Emojis that are the same in the rows below.

#BeYourself

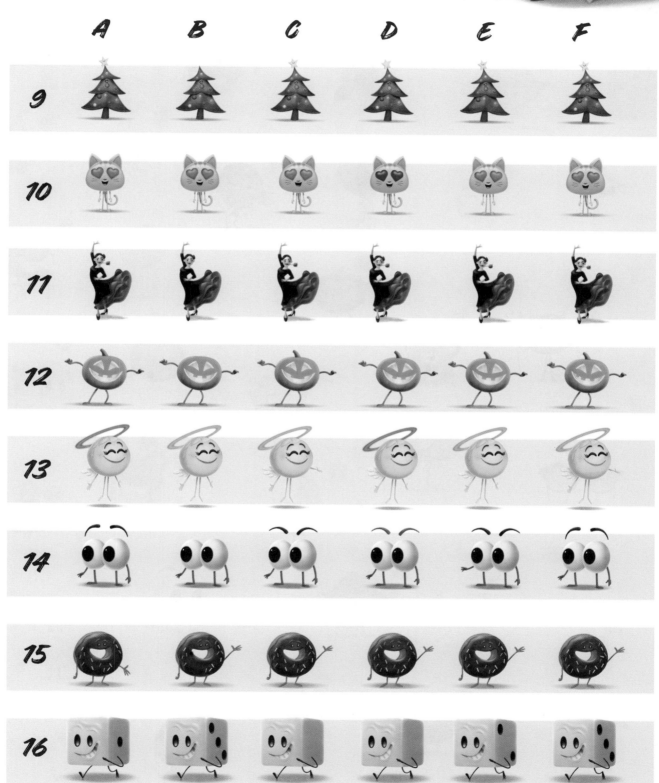

Find the answers on page 60.

Double trouble

The Emojis have doubled in numbers! Can you match them into pairs?

Can you circle the Emoji who doesn't have a match?

Find the answers on page 60.

Hide and seek

Can you find the Emojis below in the word grid opposite?

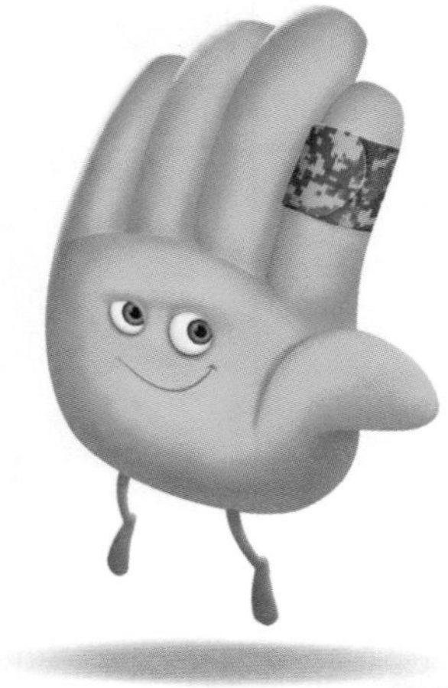

- DONUT
- BICEP
- ALIEN
- GENE
- MARY
- MEL
- SMILER

- JAILBREAK
- HI-5
- POOP DADDY
- PIZZA
- BATHTUB
- WIND
- LIPS

I DONUT care!

C R K W L O A W Q B O K Q P **H**
L D Y A N A F H U Z Y I P J I
I P W T E H C **T** P R D L K Z 5
E S F I G R H O A R B P B M T
N G Q C N T B M O I M Q E Y T
A W E W A D O **L** X K Z B **N** D Y
B G D B P S U L I I I Z E D Y
A K O A O K N L G P W E G A M
H Z Y C N Y **E** X B U S W O D E
W J Z A J **A** I L B R E A K P L
V D **P** I B Y L F B T G Z T O U
Z A R I P M A V R K Q C I O B
M M C T U N O D F P B M O P C
E E L I H S S M I L E R H S Y
P W S B J M Q J L V H R D A F

Can you rearrange the letters in a white box to reveal a large, grey Emoji?

Find the answers on page 60.

Text it

Can you match the text abbreviations to their explanations?

RUOK

4EAE

NMU?

HAK

LMBO

BRB

DWBH

F2F

CUL

TMI

Create some of your own text shorthand in the space below.

your friend's name

your name

fave colour

fave food

34

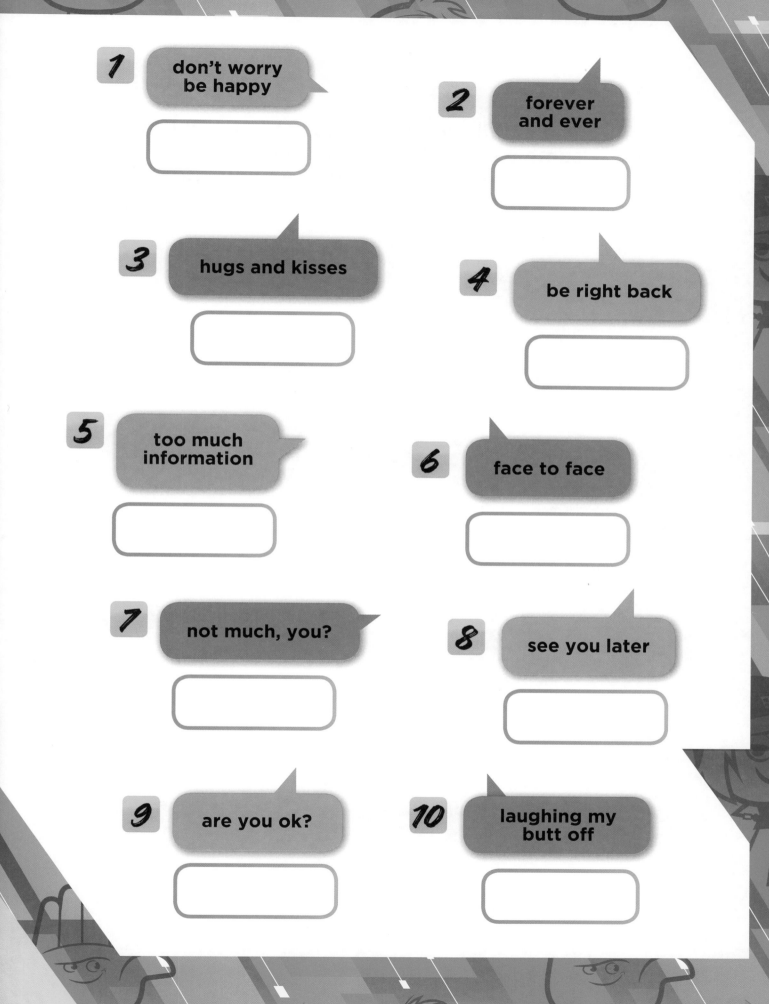

Find the answers on page 61.

The small pictures opposite may all look the same as the big picture below, but something is different in each one. Can you spot what?

Find the answers on page 61.

Emoji count up

The Emojis are everywhere, but how many do you think are on this page? Take a guess, then start counting!

Find the answers on page 61.

Being a princess stinks!

Doodle them in some different expressions and swap their colours around.

THE SKY

ISN'T THE LIMIT

LOOK OUT FOR #1

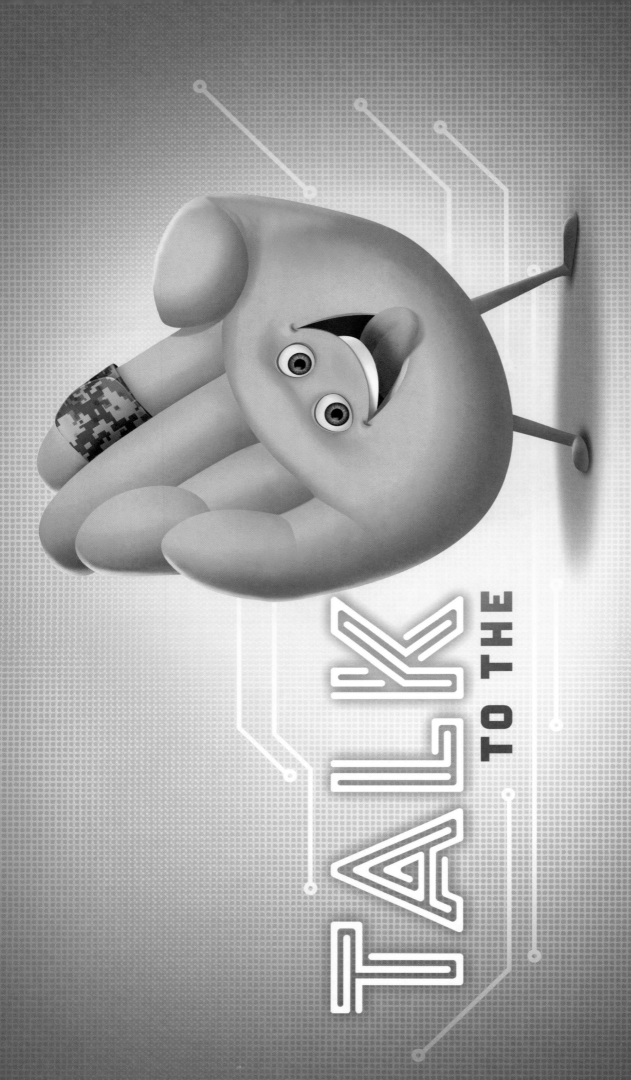

Sweet treats

Help Gene escape the candy app by showing what comes next in the sweet patterns below.

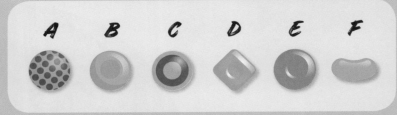

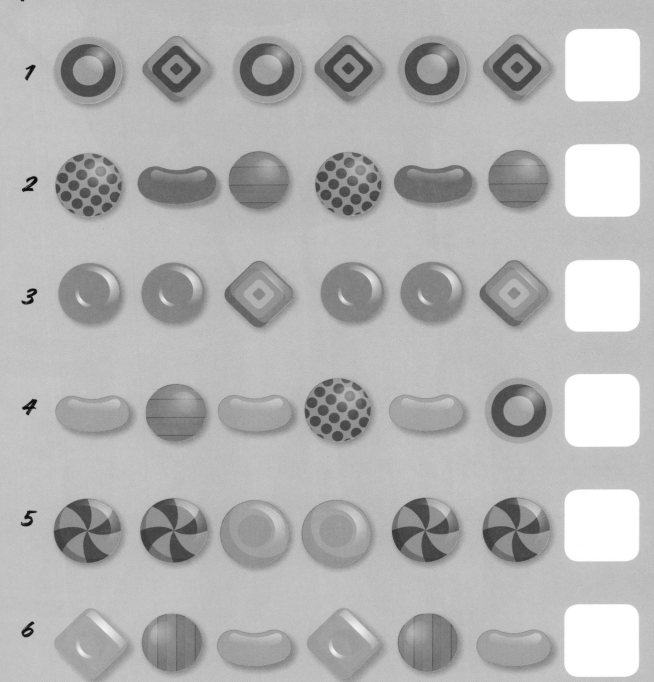

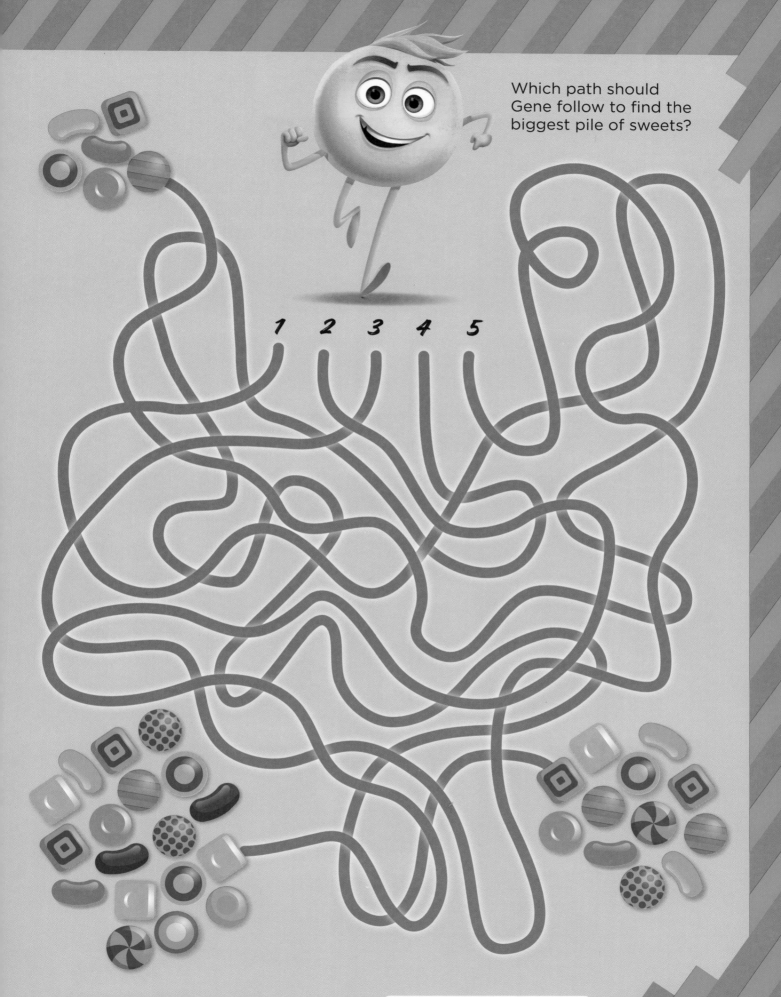

Which path should Gene follow to find the biggest pile of sweets?

1 2 3 4 5

Find the answers on page 61.

Sweet beats!

START

Help Gene and his best buds find their way through the music maze.

FINISH

Find the answers on page 61.

Where do you like to listen to music?

in your bedroom ☐

in the car ☐

on a beach ☐

in the shower ☐

Fave tune to dance to?

Top 5 groups:

....

....

....

....

Top 5 singers:

....

....

....

....

Fave tune to listen to?

#MusicRocks

How I feel about...

	pop	rock	classical	country and western
♥	☐	☐	☐	☐
👍	☐	☐	☐	☐
👽	☐	☐	☐	☐
😖	☐	☐	☐	☐

Eat, sleep, dance, repeat!

Gene sure does love to dance. Follow these simple steps to create a moving Gene, bustin' his best moves ever.

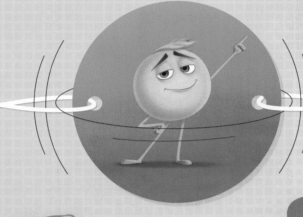

What you need:

- templates on page 61
- scissors
- hole punch
- string
- glue
- card

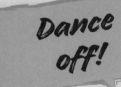

Dance off!

What you do:

1 Cut out the thaumatrope templates opposite and stick them onto some card.

2 Glue the corresponding templates together, with the images facing out.

3 Punch a hole on the left and right side of the template.

4 Tie a piece of string through each hole. Your thaumatrope should look like the finished example on this page.

5 Twist the string and let the thaumatrope spin! The two pictures should look like they are creating one single image!

6 Now try and come up with your own cool thaumatrope design.

Boogie on down

Freestyle!

Or cut out and stick these discs together to make some dance partners.

52

Keep doodling this cool pattern to fill the space below.

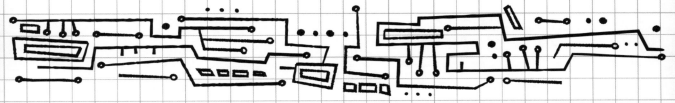

Now fill this space with lots of pixel pirates.

Cool colours

Grab your pens and add some bright colours to finish off all of these Emojis!

Wise words

Get your brain in gear and see how many of these word puzzles you can solve.

1 Colour in the letters with black hearts in them to reveal Gene's advice to all!

2

Cross out every letter that appears twice to reveal a loving Emoji.

G B H J L K D E
F W Q G B A J
L K D R F W Q T

3

Circle every third letter to reveal what Hi-5 dreams of becoming again.

G B F J L A D E V
W Q O B A U L K R
B F I Q G T D P E

4

Number these Emojis from 1 to 5 to put them in alphabetical order, then colour them in.

   1

5

How many words can you make from Jailbreak's catchphrase?

Look out for Number One!

bun, book, took, fork,

Find the answers on page 61.

Challenge!

Are you up for the Emoji Challenge? How quickly do you think you can name all these Emojis? On your marks, get set... GO!

Write your favourite Emoji's name here

58

Too easy? Ok, now close your eyes and see if you can remember every single Emoji on this page!

Find the answers on page 61.

Answers

P10-11

P12-13

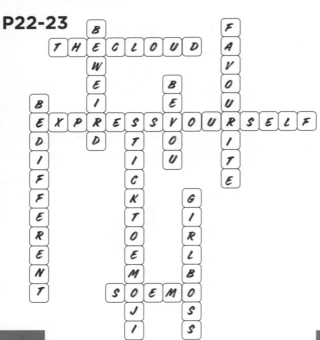

P18-19

Path 2 leasds to Hi-5
Path 5 leads to the AV-Bot
Path 4 to Smiler

P22-23

P28

1=D 2=B 3=E 4=D
5=E 6=B 7=F 8=D

P29

9=A+C 10=B+F 11=D+E
12=A+D 13=B+E 14=A+F
15=C+F 16=B+F

P30-31

1+63, 2+43, 3+ 23, 4+ 17, 5+24, 6+51,
7+40, 8+32, 9+25, 10+49, 11+61,
12+53, 13+52, 14+69, 15+29, 16+66,
18+47, 19+64, 20+59, 21+33, 22+57,
26+55, 27+48, 28+62, 30+46, 31+44,
34 +58, 35+50, 36+42, 37+67, 38+45,
39+56, 41+70, 54+65, 68+71
Wind is the Emoji with no pair

P32-33

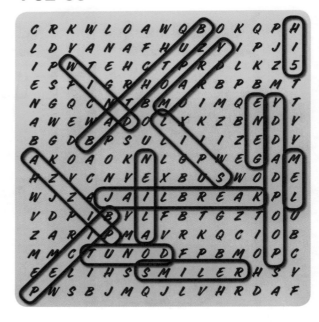

ELEPHANT is the large grey Emoji.

60

P34-35

1 =DWBH
2 = 4EAE
3= HAK
4= BRB
5= TMI
6= F2F
7=NMU?
8=CUL
9=RUOK
10=LMBO

P36-37

P48

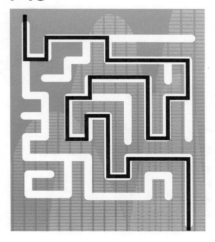

P56-57

1 Express Yourself
2 Heart
3 Favourite
4

3 2 1 4 5

5. Words could include: bun, took, for, fork, four, lot, let, loot, root, tool, rule, numb, on, but, bore, robot, no, not

P38-39

There are 80 Emojis on the page

P46-47

1=C 2=A 3=E 4=F 5=B 6=D
Gene needs to follow path 2

P58-59

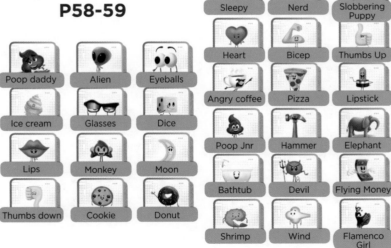